First Recorder Boo

Popular Tunes

Mary Thompson
Illustrated by Jan McCafferty

This recorder book belongs to:

....

....

Chester Music Limited
(a division of Music Sales Limited)
8/9 Frith Street, London W1V 5TZ

Love Me Tender

Love me ten-der, love me sweet, ne-ver let me go.

You have made my life com-plete, and I love you so.

Love me ten-der, love me true, all my dreams ful-filled.

For my dar-lin' I love you, and I al-ways will.

Why not colour in the pictures each time you learn a new tune?

Can-Can

once you have learned all the notes, try playing this as fast as you can.

Scarborough Fair

Are you go - ing to Scar - bor -ough Fair?

Par -sley, sage, rose - mar -y and thyme, _____ Re -

-mem - ber me to one who lives there, _____

She once was a true love of mine. _____

Blow very gently when you play low C.

Wooden Heart

Can't you see I love you Please don't break my heart in two

That's not hard to do 'Cause I don't have a wood-en heart.

___ And if you say good-bye Then I know that I would cry

May-be I would die 'Cause I don't have a wood-en heart.___

O Sole Mio

Ob-La-Di, Ob-La-Da

Des-mond had a bar-row in the mar-ket place, Mol-ly is the

sing-er in a band. Des-mond says to Mol-ly "Girl I like your face,"

And Mol-ly says this as she takes him by the hand. Ob-la-di, ob-la-da,

life goes on bra. La - la how life goes on.

Show Me The Way To Go Home

Show me the way to go home, I'm tired and I want to go to bed. I

had a lit-tle drink a-bout an hour a-go And it went right to my head. No

mat-ter where I roam, O'er land or sea or foam, You will

al-ways hear me sing-ing this song, Show me the way to go home.

Remember, A sharp is the same as B flat.

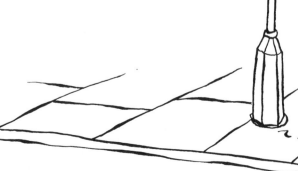

The Sound Of Silence

When You Wish Upon A Star

When you wish up - on a star Makes no differ-ence who you are.

An - y - thing your heart de - sires Will come to you.

If your heart is in your dream No re - quest is too ex - treme.

When you wish up - on a star As dream - ers do.

Santa Lucia

G flat is the same as f sharp.

Nellie The Elephant

To Bom - bay a tra-vel-ling cir-cus came, they

brought an in-tell-i-gent el-e-phant and Nel-lie was her name__

One dark night she slipped her iron__ chain and

off she ran to Hin-dus-tan and was nev-er seen a - gain.

Nel - lie the el - e - phant packed her trunk and said good-bye to the

cir - cus. Off she went with a trum-pe- ty trump, trump, trump,

trump. Now Nel - lie the el - e - phant packed her trunk and

trun - dled off to the jung - le. Off she went with a

trum- pe- ty trump, trump, trump, trump._____

What Shall We Do With The Drunken Sailor

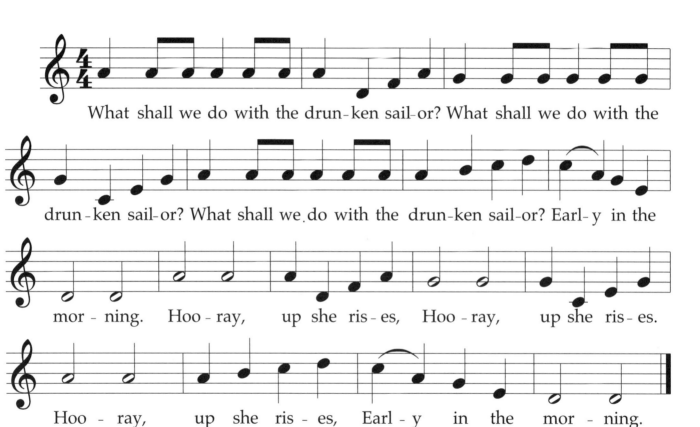

What shall we do with the drun-ken sail-or? What shall we do with the

drun-ken sail-or? What shall we do with the drun-ken sail-or? Earl-y in the

mor - ning. Hoo - ray, up she ris - es, Hoo - ray, up she ris - es.

Hoo - ray, up she ris - es, Earl - y in the mor - ning.

She'll Be Coming Round The Mountain

She'll be com-ing round the moun-tain when she comes._ She'll be

com-ing round the moun-tain when she comes._____ She'll be

com-ing round the moun-tain, Com-ing round the moun-tain. She'll be

com - ing round the moun-tain when she comes._____

Mexican Hat Dance

Yellow Submarine

In the town _ where I was born   Lived a man ___ who sailed to
sailed _ up to the sun,   'Til we found ___ the sea of

sea   And he told _ us of his life   In the land _____ of sub-mar-
green   And we lived _ be-neath the waves   In our

- ines.   So we   yel - low sub-mar - ine.   We all live in a

yel - low sub - mar - ine,   yel - low sub - mar - ine,   yel - low sub - mar - ine.

I Wan'na Be Like You

Now I'm the king of the swing-ers the jun-gle V - I - P I've

reached the top and had to stop And that's what's both-er-in' me. I

wan-na be a man, man-cub And stroll right in-to town. And

be just like the oth-er men I'm tired of mon-keyin' a - round! Oh,

Going from G sharp to F sharp is a bit tricky, so you might need to practise it separately.

Danse Des Mirlitons

Remember to pause on the top G at the end of the second line.

I'd Do Anything

The Sailor's Hornpipe

Love Me Tender

Words & music by Elvis Presley & Vera Matson
© Copyright 1956 Elvis Presley Music, USA. Carlin Music Corporation, Iron Bridge House, 3 Bridge
Approach, London NW1 for the territory of United Kingdom of Great Britain & Northern Ireland,
Eire, Israel & the British Dominions, Colonies, Overseas Territories & Dependencies
(excluding Canada, Australia and New Zealand).

All Rights Reserved. International Copyright Secured.

Wooden Heart

Words & music by Fred Wise, Ben Weisman, Kay Twomey & Bert Kaempfert
© Copyright 1960 Gladys Music, New York, USA.
Carlin Music Corporation, Iron Bridge House, 3 Bridge Approach, London NW1 for the United
Kingdom of Great Britain and Northern Ireland, Eire, Israel and the British Dominions, Colonies,
Overseas Territories & Dependencies (excluding Canada, Australia & New Zealand).

All Rights Reserved. International Copyright Secured.

Ob-La-Di, Ob-La-Da

Words & music by John Lennon & Paul McCartney
© Copyright 1968 Northern Songs.
All Rights Reserved. International Copyright Secured.

Show Me The Way To Go Home

Words & music by Irving King & Hal Swain
© Copyright 1925 Campbell Connelly & Company Limited,
8/9 Frith Street, London W1.

All Rights Reserved. International Copyright Secured.

The Sound Of Silence

Words & music by Paul Simon
© Copyright 1964 Paul Simon.
All Rights Reserved. International Copyright Secured.

When You Wish Upon A Star

Words by Ned Washington, Music by Leigh Harline
© Copyright 1940 Bourne Company, USA. Warner Chappell Music Limited,
Griffin House, 161 Hammersmith Road, London W6.

All Rights Reserved. International Copyright Secured.

Nellie The Elephant

Words by Ralph Butler
Music by Peter Hart
© Copyright 1956 Dash Music Company Limited,
8/9 Frith Street, London W1.

All Rights Reserved. International Copyright Secured.

Yellow Submarine

Words & music by John Lennon & Paul McCartney
© Copyright 1966 Northern Songs.

All Rights Reserved. International Copyright Secured.

I Wan'na Be Like You

From Walt Disney Pictures' 'The Jungle Book'
Words & music by Richard M. Sherman & Robert B. Sherman
© Copyright 1966 by Wonderland Music Company, Incorporated. Copyright renewed.
This arrangement © Copyright 1995 by Wonderland Music Company, Inc.

Used by Music Sales Limited, 8/9 Frith Street, London W1 with permission.

I'd Do Anything

Words & music by Lionel Bart
© Copyright 1959 by Lakeview Music Publishing Company Limited,
Suite 2.07, Plaza 535 Kings Road, London SW10.
All Rights Reserved. International Copyright Secured.